WINSTON FAMILY PAPERDOLLS

Illustrated by

BLYTHE RUSSO

Based on the Novels by
NEW YORK TIMES BEST SELLING AUTHOR

PENNY REID

Copyright

A Letter from the Illustrator

It was sometime in 2016 and I was chatting with a group of my amazing author-illustrator friends - all of whom were also romance readers. One of them (or maybe a few of them) had recommended me to read Penny Reid's Knitting in the City series.

So, I read Janie's book and then quickly devoured the next one, and the next, until I hit Ashley's book. By that time I was completely hooked, but there was something different about Beauty and the Mustache. I loved Ashley. I loved Drew. But I LOVED Ashley's brothers - the Winston's.

And then I found out, from that same group of women, that Penny had started a series focusing on those brothers. A series about handsome, bearded, lumberjack men? Yes, please. Where do I sign?

See, something to know about me is I love lumberjacks. I don't know when or why or how it started, but it's a whole thing. Buffalo plaid, and log cabins, and beards - oh my! So the Winston Brothers series was right up my alley.

I immediately gobbled up the first two books in the series and eagerly awaited the third installment.

Fast forward to August 2018, when a friend from that same romance-reading group (noticing a trend?), told me about some Turkish show she had started watching. (I guess the show already had a bit of a following in Penny's Sharks of Awesome FB group and that's how said friend had heard about it.) I ended up watching the first episode and was completely hooked. (Apparently, I am easily hooked.) So I joined Penny's FB group and then joined the subgroup for the Turkish show, Erkenci Kus or EK.

Yadda yadda yadda, a couple episodes into the series, I made some EK fan art and shared it with the group. And then turned that fan art into paper dolls for Festivus gifts and shared those with the group.

Ultimately, Penny saw them, loved them, and asked me to give the same paper doll treatment to the Winston Brothers.

And here we are today.

So, I would like to thank Penny for allowing me the opportunity to illustrate her beloved Winston brothers (and a bunch of other characters in the Green Valley community). As a fan of the books myself, it was an honor to be trusted to visually bring them to life and I had a lot of fun doing so. I know everyone imagines the characters in different ways as they read, so I hope I did them - and your imaginations - justice.

Best wishes and enjoy,

Blythe

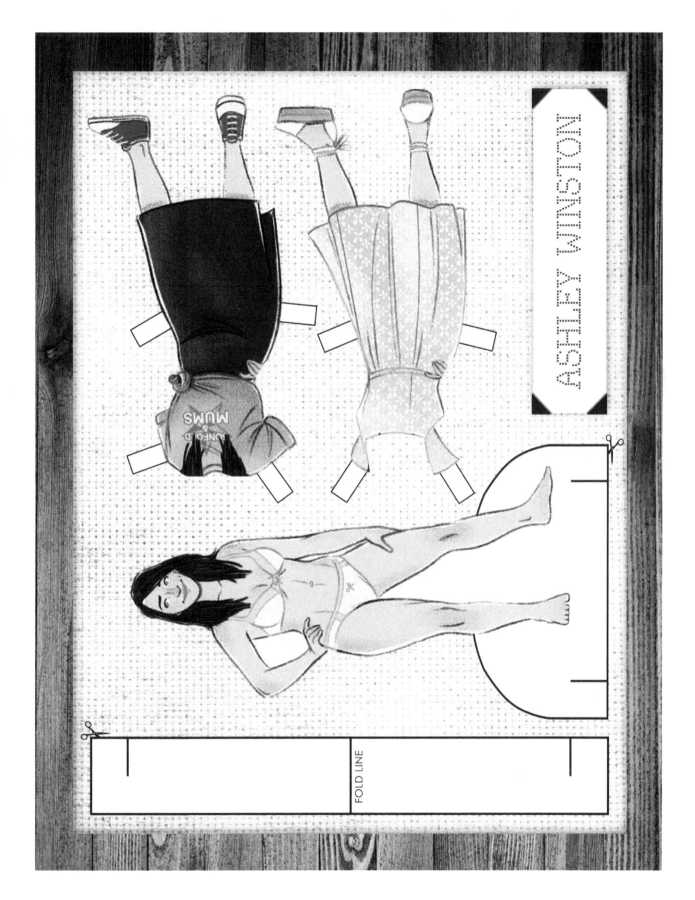

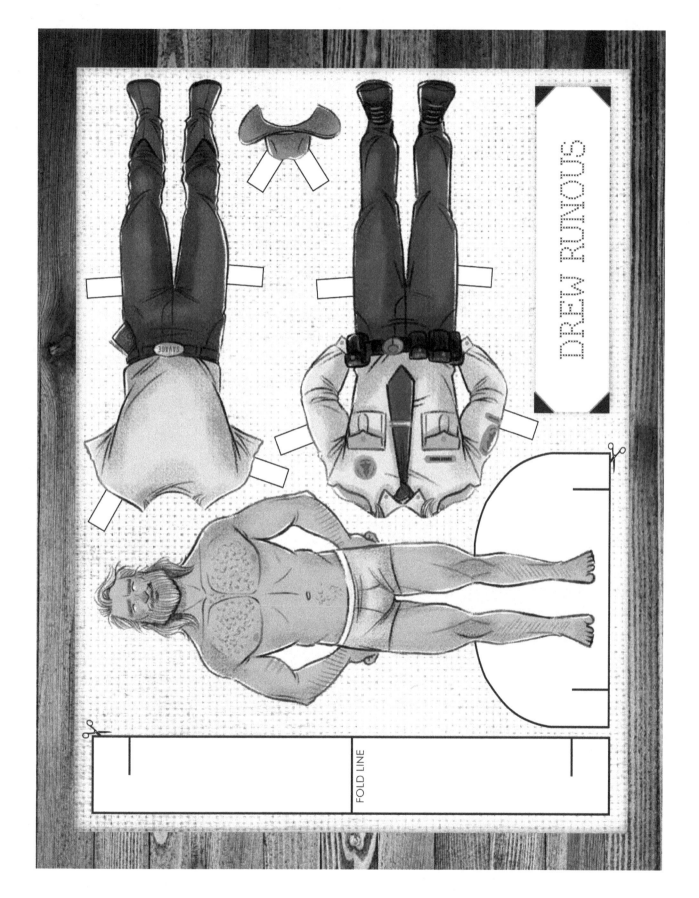

DREW RIVOLS

FOLD LINE

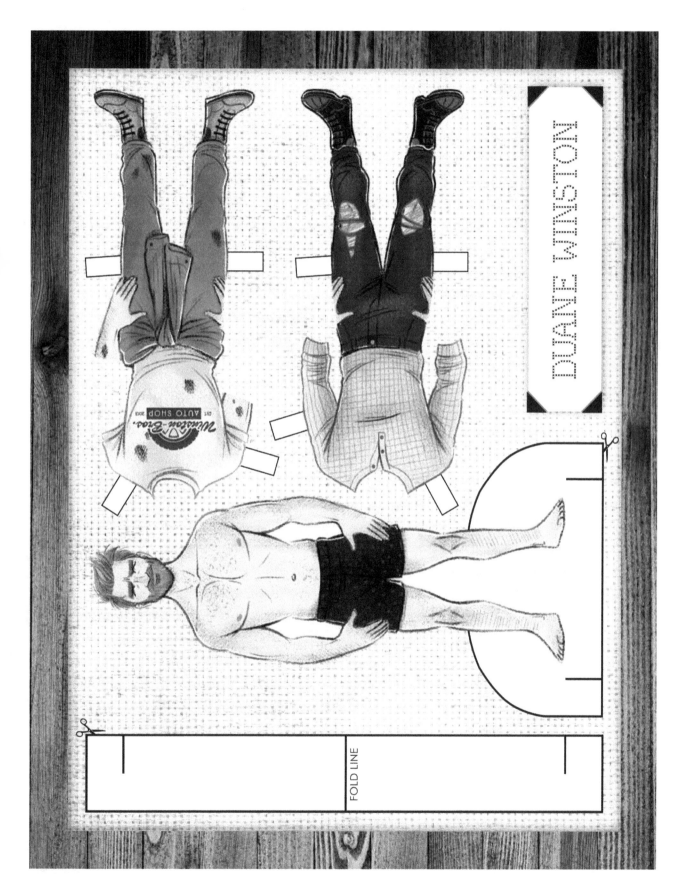

DUANE WINSTON

FOLD LINE

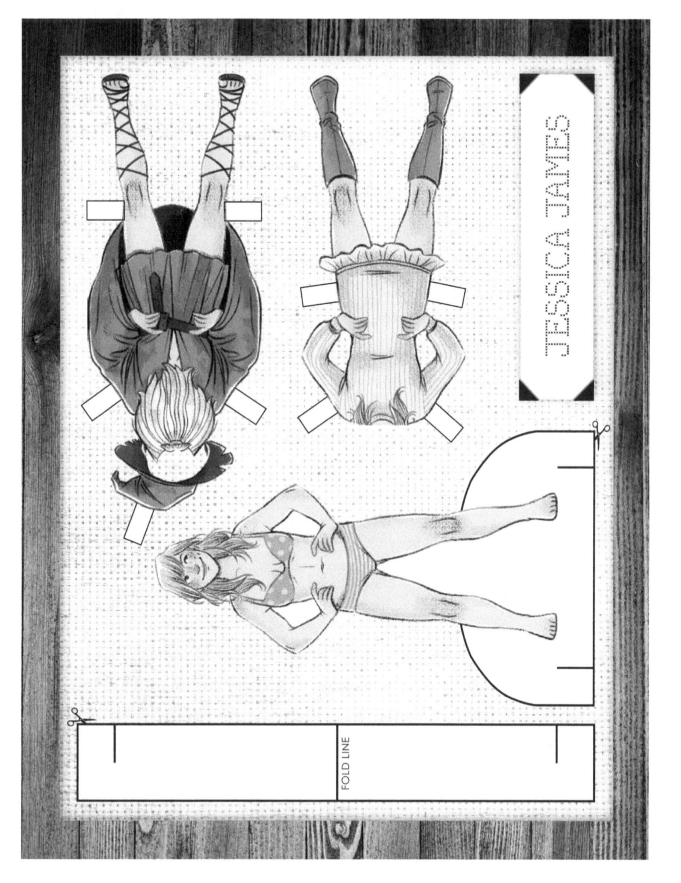

JESSICA JAMES

FOLD LINE

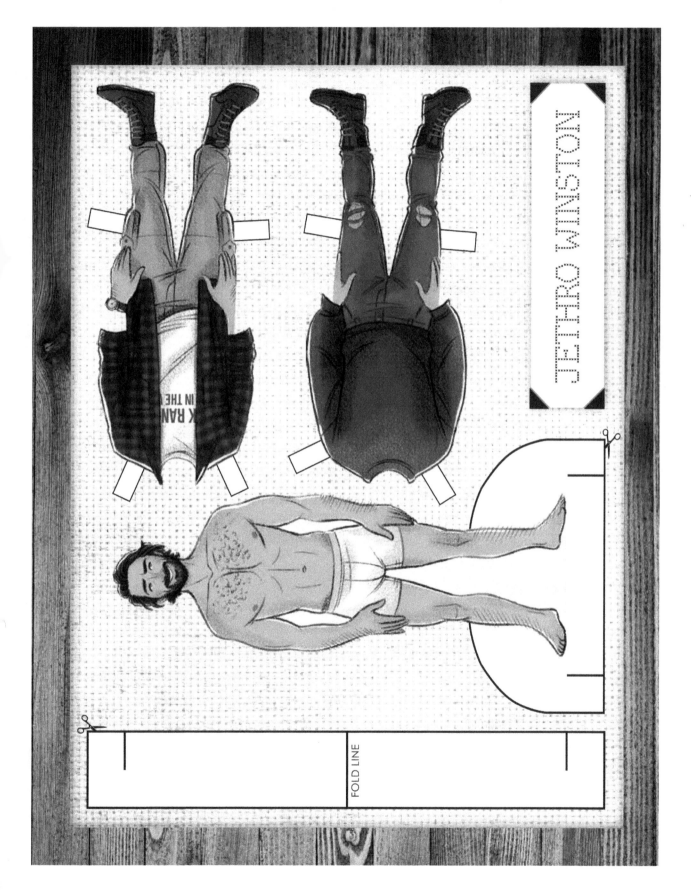

JETHRO WINSTON

FOLD LINE

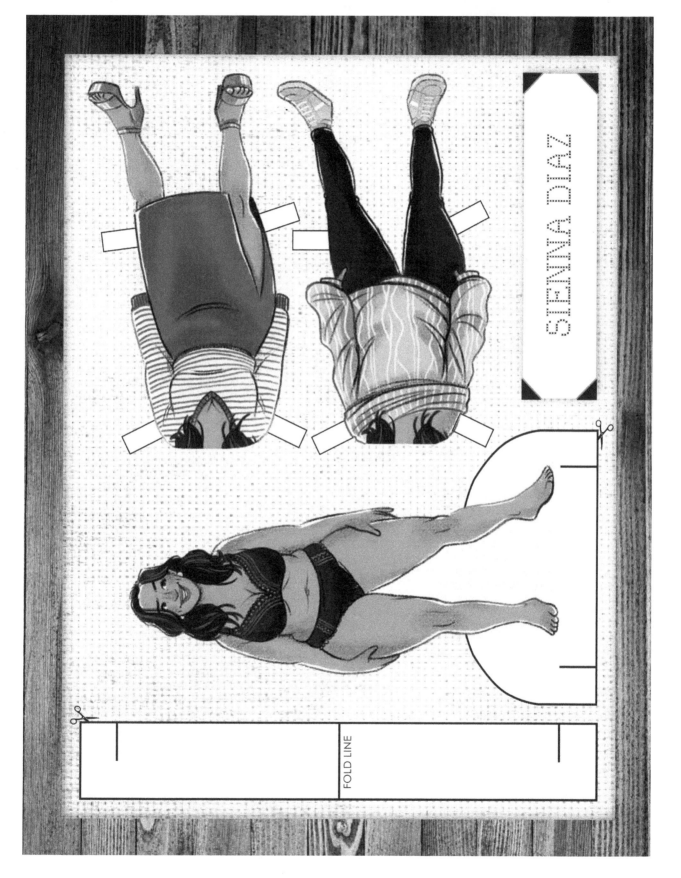

SIENNA DIAZ

FOLD LINE

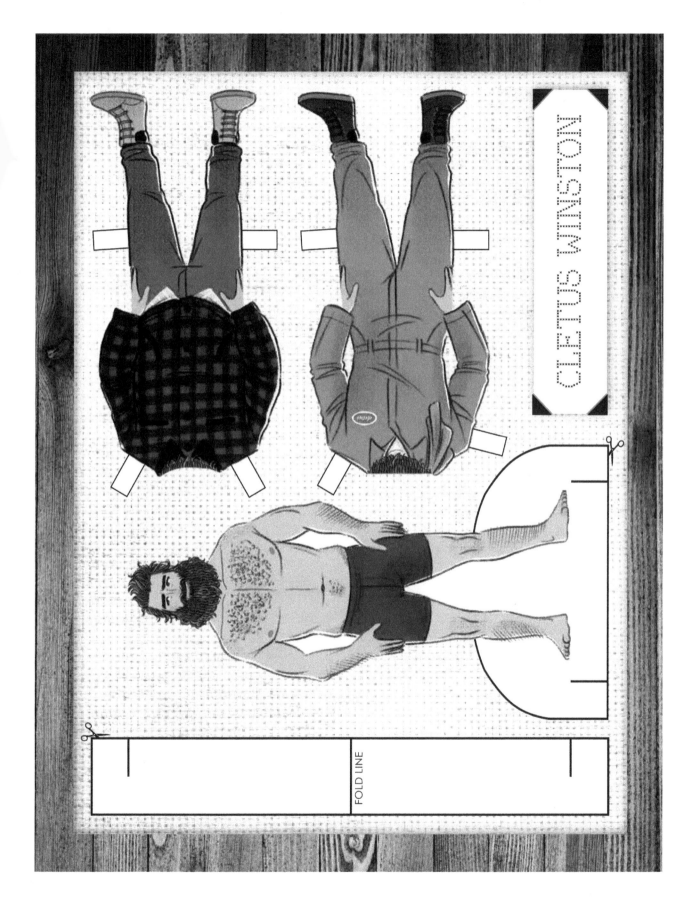

CLETUS WINSTON

FOLD LINE

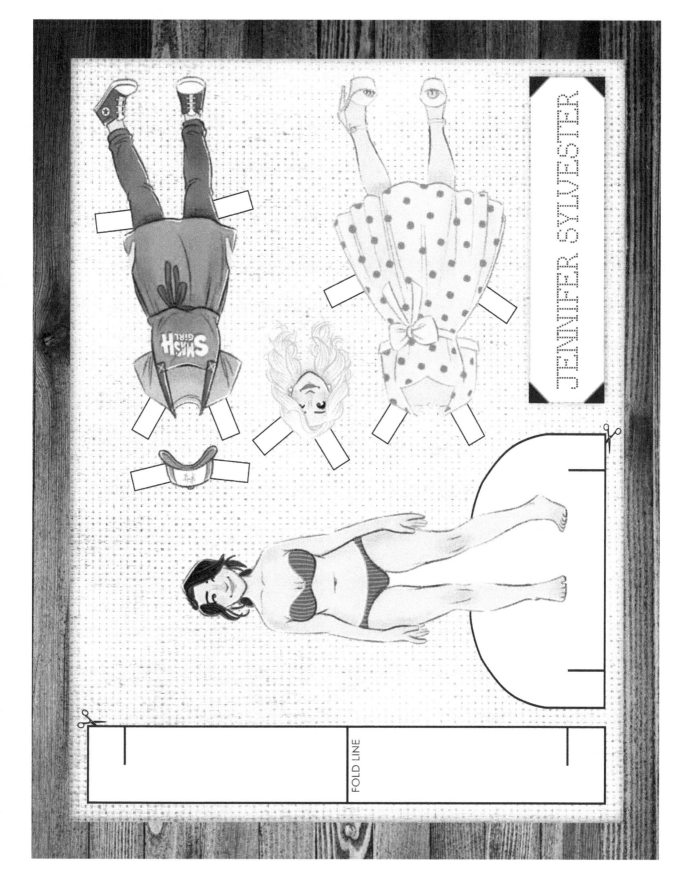

JENNIFER SYLVESTER

SWISH GIRL

FOLD LINE

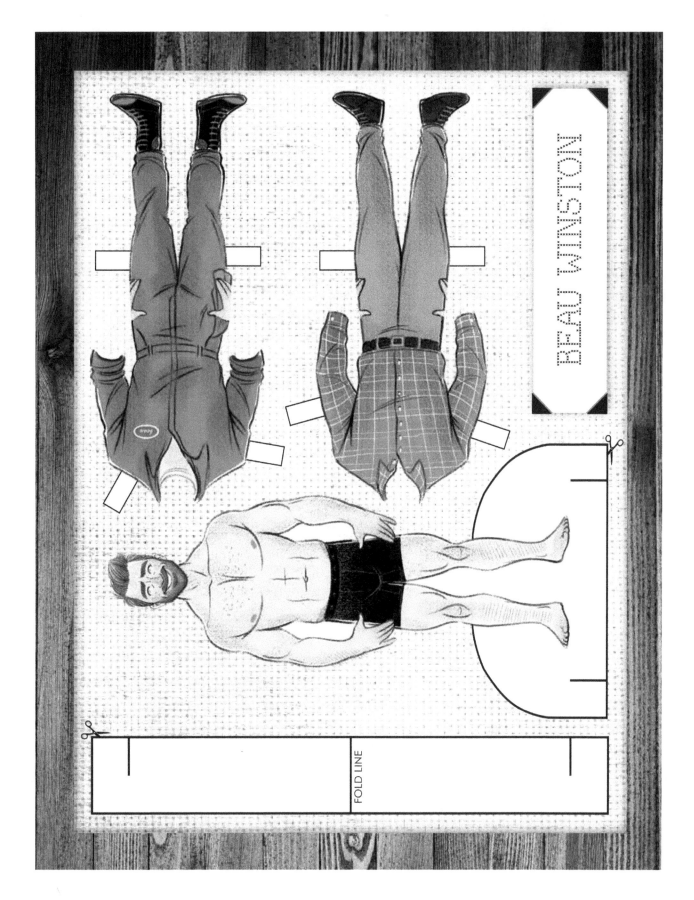

BEAT WILSTON

FOLD LINE

SHELLY SILLTAN

FOLD LINE

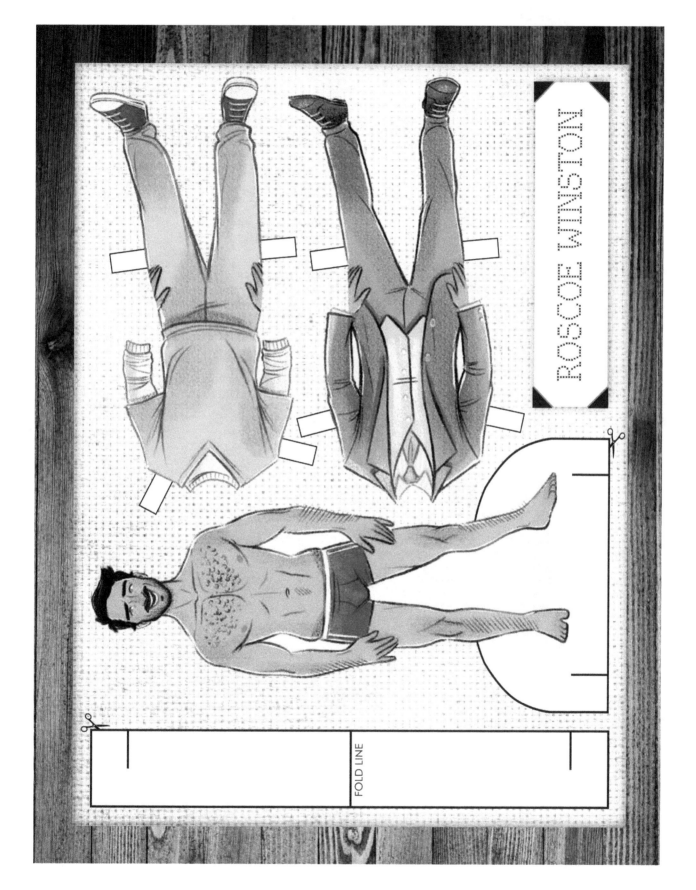

ROSCOE WINSTON

FOLD LINE

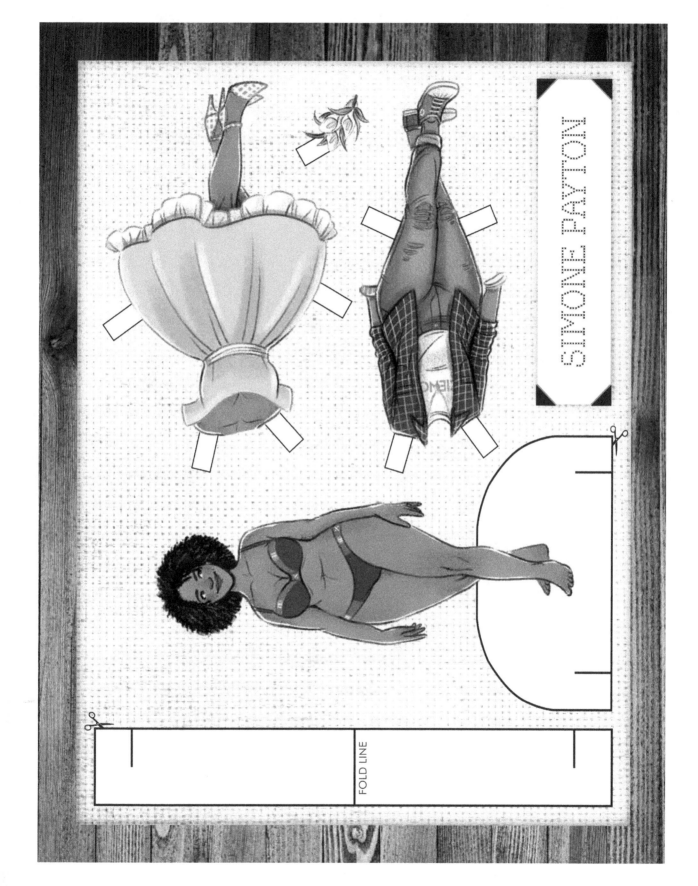

SIMONE PAYTON

FOLD LINE

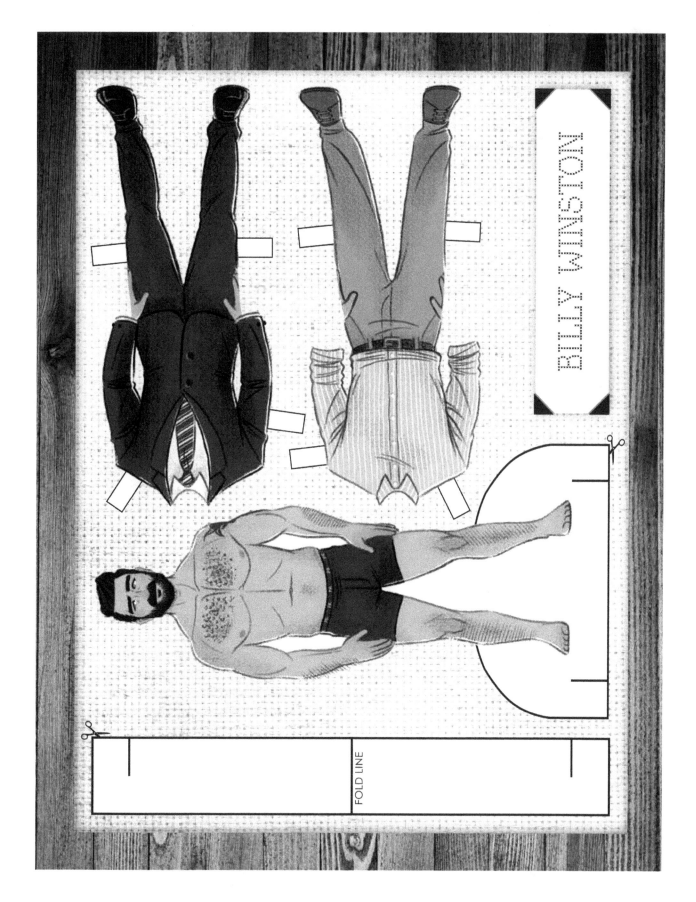

BILLY MINSTON

FOLD LINE

CLAIRE MCCLURE

FOLD LINE

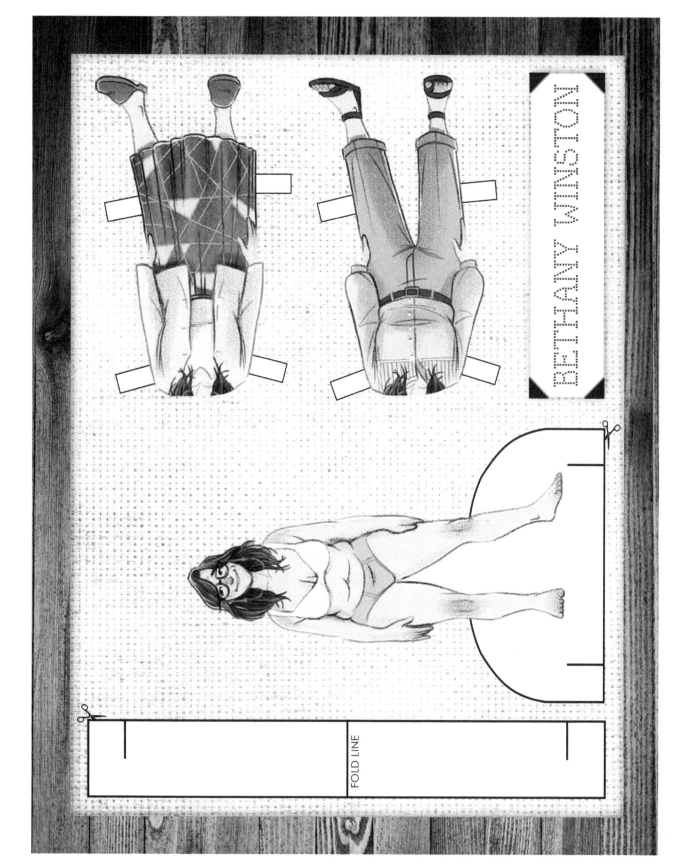

BETHANY WINSTON

FOLD LINE

About the Illustrator

Blythe is an author-illustrator currently living just outside Cincinnati, Ohio. When she's not busy making books, you can find her sewing, building puppets, or in the kitchen on a never-ending quest for the perfect chocolate chip cookie recipe.

Website: www.blytherussoillustration.com
Instagram:http://instagram.com/blythe_russo
Twitter: http://www.twitter.com/blythe_russo

Publications

ONE MORE WHEEL

Written by Colleen AF Venable; illustrated by Blythe Russo

About the Author of the Winston Brothers

Penny Reid is the *New York Times*, *Wall Street Journal*, and *USA Today* Bestselling Author of the Winston Brothers, Knitting in the City, Rugby, Dear Professor, and Hypothesis series. She used to spend her days writing federal grant proposals as a biomedical researcher, but now she just writes books. She's also a full time mom to three diminutive adults, wife, daughter, knitter, crocheter, sewer, general crafter, and thought ninja.

Mailing List: http://pennyreid.ninja/newsletter/
Facebook: www.facebook.com/pennyreidwriter
Twitter: www.twitter.com/reidromance
Instagram: www.instagram.com/reidromance

Penny Reid's Booklist

Knitting in the City Series
(Interconnected Standalones, Adult Contemporary Romantic Comedy)
Neanderthal Seeks Human: A Smart Romance (#1)
Neanderthal Marries Human: A Smarter Romance (#1.5)
Friends without Benefits: An Unrequited Romance (#2)
Love Hacked: A Reluctant Romance (#3)
Beauty and the Mustache: A Philosophical Romance (#4)
Ninja at First Sight (#4.75)
Happily Ever Ninja: A Married Romance (#5)
Dating-ish: A Humanoid Romance (#6)
Marriage of Inconvenience (#7)
Neanderthal Seeks Extra Yarns (#8)
Knitting in the City Coloring Book (#9)

Winston Brothers Series
(Interconnected Standalones, Adult Contemporary Romantic Comedy, spinoff of *Beauty and the Mustache*)
Beauty and the Mustache (#0.5)
Truth or Beard (#1)
Grin and Beard It (#2)
Beard Science (#3)
Beard in Mind (#4)
Dr. Strange Beard (#5)
Beard with Me (#6)
Beard Necessities (#7)
A Beardy Bonus (#8)

Hypothesis Series
(New Adult Romantic Comedy Trilogies)
Elements of Chemistry: ATTRACTION, HEAT, and CAPTURE (#1)
Laws of Physics: MOTION, SPACE, and TIME (#2)

Irish Players (Rugby) Series – by L.H. Cosway and Penny Reid
(Interconnected Standalones, Adult Contemporary Sports Romance)
The Hooker and the Hermit (#1)
The Pixie and the Player (#2)
The Cad and the Co-ed (#3)
The Varlet and the Voyeur (#4)

Dear Professor Series
(New Adult Romantic Comedy)

Kissing Tolstoy (#1)
Kissing Galileo (#2)

Ideal Man Series
(Interconnected Standalones, Adult Contemporary Romance Series of Jane Austen Reimaginings)
Pride and Dad Jokes (#1, coming 2021)
Man Buns and Sensibility (#2, TBD)
Sense and Manscaping (#3, TBD)
Persuasion and Man Hands (#4, TBD)
Mantuary Abbey (#5, TBD)
Mancave Park (#6, TBD)
Emmanuel (#7, TBD)

Penny Reid's Booklist

Solving for Pie: Cletus and Jenn Mysteries Series
(A Romantic Cozy Mystery Series, spinoff of The Winston Brothers Series)
Engagement and Espionage (#1)
Marriage and Murder (#2, coming 2021)
Home and Heist (#3, coming 2022)
Baby and Ballistics (#4, coming 2023)
Pie Crimes and Misdemeanors (TBD)

Good Folks Series
(Interconnected Standalones, Adult Contemporary Romantic Comedy, spinoff of The Winston Brothers Series)
Totally Folked (#1, coming 2021)
Give a Folk (#2, coming 2022)

Three Kings Series
(Interconnected Standalones, Holiday-themed Adult Contemporary Romantic Comedies)
Homecoming King (#1, coming Christmas 2021)
Drama King (#2, coming Christmas 2022)
Prom King (#3, coming Christmas 2023)

CPSIA information can be obtained
at www.ICGtesting.com
Printed in the USA
LVHW012014051122
732161LV00002B/16